Contents

Lost in the park

Peter was lost in the big park.

He could not find his mother.

He looked and looked but he could not find her.

Then he saw a police car.

He put out his hand. The car stopped.

"What is it?" said the policeman.

"I don't know where my mum is.

She's lost in the park," said Peter.

"I can help you," said the policeman.
'What's your name?"

"My name is Peter. Peter Hill. I am six. I live in West Street."

"In you get," said the policeman. "Let's call the police station."
The policeman talked on his radio.

"Hello, hello. Peter Hill has lost his mother in the park. He is six, and he lives in West Street." Peter sat and waited.

Soon the policeman said, "Your mother is waiting for you at the police station, Peter."

"Can I ride with you?" said Peter.

"Yes," said the policeman.

"This is fun," said Peter.

Peter saw his mother.

"Hello, Mum," said Peter. "Where did you go?"

"Hello, Peter," said Mum. "I lost you in the park."

"And I lost you," said Peter. "But I found a policeman. He let me ride in his car!"

Mum said "Thank you" to the policeman.

The policeman said, "We like to help lost boys. We like to help lost mothers, too."

Buildings

This is an old bridge which goes over the river.
Cars come over this bridge to get to the town.
Can you think why all these people are coming
into town?

This big building is a car park.

Some people are going to put their cars in it and then they will go to the shops.

When they want to go back home, they will come back to the car park and get the cars.

This new bridge goes over the road.

People go over it to get from the car park to

the shops. Look at all the people who have

come into town.

Do you think they are all going shopping?

Cars can't go down this street.

It is just for people who are going to the shops.

There are lots of buildings in this street.

Some are old and some are new.

Some are big and some are small.

Look at this building. It's a book shop.

Some children have stopped to look at
the books.

The boy would like the one about animals.

The girl wants a book about helicopters.

The cake shop is not as big as the book shop

but there are lots and lots of cakes in it.

Don't they look good?

Which one would you like?

At the end of the street there is a
very old building. It's a house.
People don't live in it now but
lots of people like to go and look at it.
Does it look like the house you live in?

This building is a radio station.

People from the radio station sometimes go

out into the street to talk to people.

This building is a police station.

Lots of people work in it.

They are there to help us.

Can you see a policeman going into the building?

Do you think that car in the street is his?

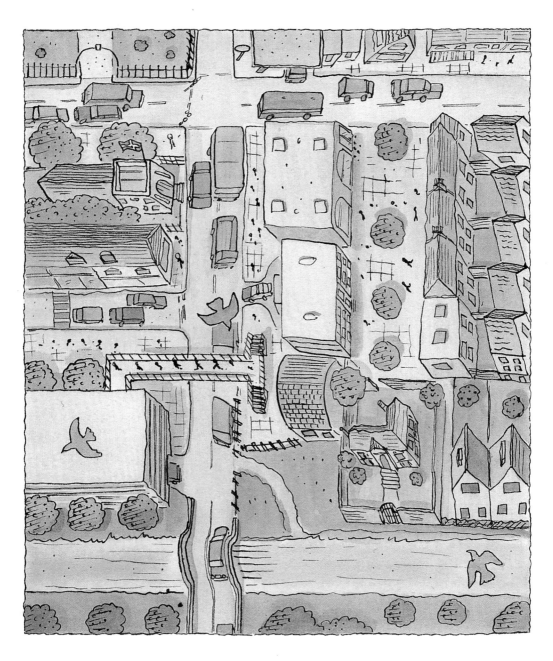

Look at all the buildings in the town.

Can you say what they are?

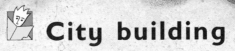 City building

Feet on the street
and head in the sky,
my windows
watch the clouds go by.

Busy city people
hurry through my doors,
ride in the lift
to sixteen floors.

At night on my rooftop
birds sit in rows,
and a mouse on the pavement
tickles my toes.

Irene Rawnsley

New shoes

James said, "Mum, can I have some new shoes, please?"

"Yes," said Mum. "You need some new shoes." They went to the shop.

"We need some new shoes for James," said Mum.

James said, "I have some old shoes at home.
But they are too small for me."

"We can find some new shoes for you, James,"
said the man. "Come with me."

James and Mum looked at the shoes.

James said, "Mum, can I have these shoes, please?"

"Yes," said Mum.

Penny said, "Will you get new shoes
for me, too?"

"No, Penny," said Mum. "You can't have new
shoes now. Your shoes are not too small."

The man said, "Here is a balloon for you.
It comes with the new shoes."

"Thank you," said James.
James looked at Penny.
"I have some new shoes," he said.
"Would you like the balloon?"

"Yes, please," said Penny. "Now I have
something new! Thank you, James."

James said, "I like my new shoes."

Penny said, "I like my red balloon, too."

"Don't play with the balloon in here," said Mum.

"You can play with it at home."

Mum and James went on.

They did not see where Penny went.

Penny saw a woman with a dog.

"Hello, little dog," said Penny. "Do you like
my red balloon?"
The dog gave Penny a surprise. He ran away
with the balloon. He surprised the woman, too.

Penny said, "Stop! Stop! Where are you going
with my balloon?"

The woman said, "Stop, Snowy. You come here!"

Snowy did not stop.

He was running very fast.

Penny said, "My balloon! The dog can't have it."

The woman went to find Snowy.

But she did not know where to look.

Then Penny saw Mum.

"Mum!" she said. "The dog has got my balloon!

The woman is looking for her dog. She wants

to find Snowy. But I want my red balloon."

Mum, James and Penny went to look for Snowy.
But they could not find him.

A man asked, "Are you looking for something?"

"Yes, we are," said Mum. "We are looking for
a dog with a red balloon."

"A dog?" asked the man. "A dog with a balloon?"

"Can you help us find him?" asked Penny.
"We don't know where he went."

"I can see him!" said James.

The woman saw Snowy too. But Penny saw
the balloon.

"My balloon!" she said. "Look at my balloon!
Now I can't play with it."

Mum said, "We can get you a new
balloon, Penny."

"We have some animal balloons,"
said the man in the shop.

"Animal balloons?" asked Penny.
"I like animal balloons."

Then the woman came up and said,
"Let me get a balloon for Penny."

Penny looked at the animal balloons, and she saw a dog. She saw a big dog balloon.

The woman asked, "Do you like the balloon? You may have it, Penny."

"Thank you," said Penny. "Now you have found Snowy. And I have a dog, too."